BOUNCING AND BENDING LIGHT

Barbara Taylor

Photographs by Peter Millard

FRANKLIN WATTS
London • New York • Sydney • Toronto

Design: Janet Watson

Science consultant: Dr Bryson Gore

Educational consultants: Kay Davies and
Wendy Oldfield

Series editor: Debbie Fox

The author and publisher would like to thank the
following children for their participation in the
photography of this book: Eleanor Kingsbury,
Sarah Knight, Leo Thomson, William Mosse,
Christakis Phillipou and Kate Jones.

Franklin Watts
96 Leonard Street
London EC2A 4RH

Franklin Watts Inc.
387 Park Avenue South
New York
NY 10016

Franklin Watts Australia
14 Mars Road
Lane Cove
NSW 2066

UK ISBN: 0 86313 883 7

Printed in Belgium

Safety
● Never stare at the Sun or any bright light. You could
damage your eyes.
● Take care with all mirrors and lenses. Plastic
mirrors are safest, but if you use unframed glass
mirrors, tape the edges and put a cross of tape on the
back. This will stop you cutting your fingers or
chipping the mirror.

CONTENTS

This book is all about the reflection and
refraction of light. It is divided into five
sections. Each has a different coloured
triangle at the corner of the page. Use
these triangles to help you find the
different sections.

These red triangles at the corner of the
tinted panels show you where a step-by-
step investigation starts.

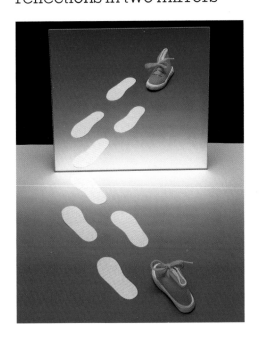

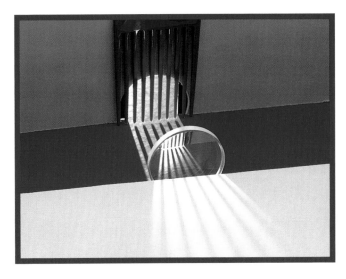

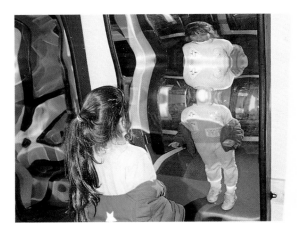

LIGHT ON THE MOVE

Look at the sunlight shining through these trees. What shape are the edges of the rays of light?

They are straight lines. Even though the rays spread out, the edges of the rays are still straight. This is one of the most important things about light. It goes straight from one place to another and does not bend around things.

To see how light travels, try this investigation.

1 Find two pieces of card and cut a hole in the centre of each piece.

2 Arrange the cards in a straight line. To help you line up the holes, put a knitting needle through both holes.

3 Fix the cards in position with corks or modelling clay.

4 In a dark room, shine a torch straight through one hole. You will find that the light goes through the other hole and comes out the other side.

What happens if the holes are not in a straight line?

To find the centre of the card, draw a line from each corner to the opposite corner. The point where the lines cross is the centre.

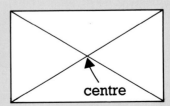

centre

SHADOWS

If light hits an object that will not let the light through, a shadow forms behind the object. The light cannot bend around the object to light up the shadow area. Materials that block out the light are said to be opaque. Try shining a torch at different materials such as brick, wood, cloth, foil, leaves, tracing paper and plastic. How many opaque materials can you find?

Your body is opaque. Can you make a monster shadow with your friends?

If you are near the light, you stop a lot of light getting through. This makes a big shadow.

If you are further away from the light, you block out less light. This makes a smaller shadow.

A shadow shows only the outline of an object.
Can you see which objects made these shadows?
Make a collection of small objects and draw
pictures of the shadows they make. Try turning
the objects around. How does this change the
shape of their shadows?

BOUNCING BACK

When light hits a surface, it bounces back from the surface. This is called reflection. Everything reflects some light. When light is reflected into our eyes, we can see things.

To find out more about reflected light, try this test.

1 Cut a hole about 2.5cm across in the bottom edge of a piece of card.

2 Fix a comb over the hole.

3 Use modelling clay to keep the card upright.

4 Use corks to hold a mirror facing the comb. Make sure the mirror is at an angle.

5 Shine a torch through the hole so the light rays hit the mirror. What happens?

When light hits a surface at a certain angle, it always bounces off at a matching angle. Change the angle of the mirror to see how this changes the angle of the reflected light rays.

Which of these materials are good at reflecting light?

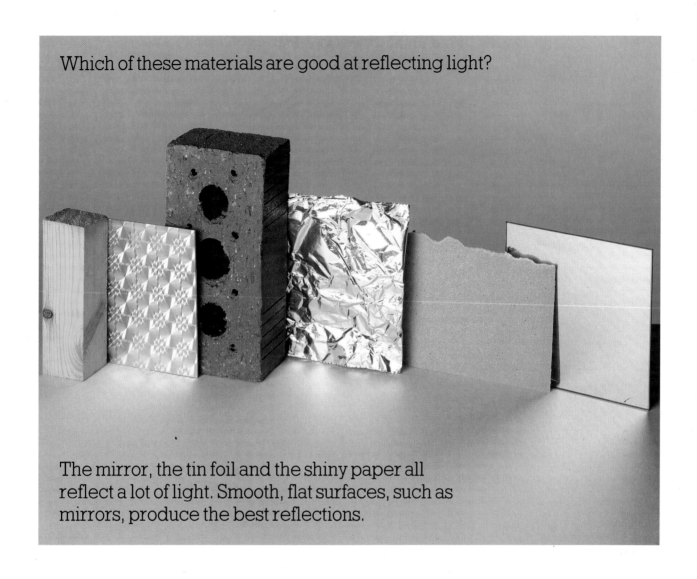

The mirror, the tin foil and the shiny paper all reflect a lot of light. Smooth, flat surfaces, such as mirrors, produce the best reflections.

▼ On a smooth surface, most of the light is reflected back in one direction.

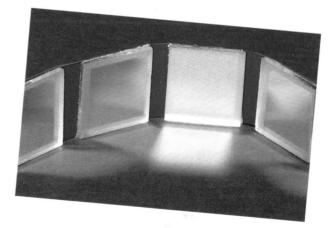

▲ On a rough surface, light is reflected back in lots of different directions. This is called scattering the light.

MIRRORS AND REFLECTIONS

How many footprints are reflected in this mirror?

All four footprints are reflected in the mirror. The reflection of the shoe seems to be as far behind the mirror as the real shoe is in front. Stand in front of a mirror and use a tape measure to see how far your reflection appears to be behind the mirror. If you move backwards and forwards, your reflection will move exactly the same distance behind the mirror.

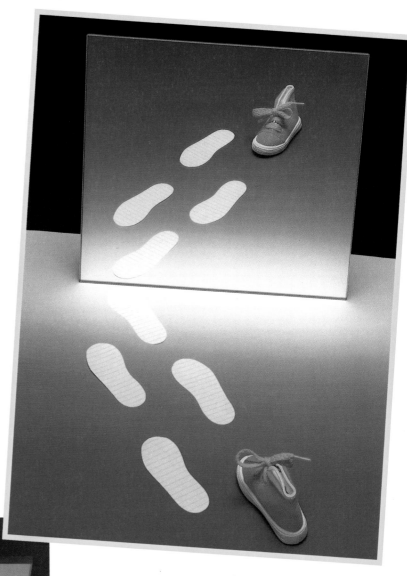

Some objects, such as this daisy, are exactly the same on both sides. They are called symmetrical objects. If you hold a mirror along the centre line of a symmetrical object, you can see the whole object. The right place to hold the mirror is called the folding line, or the line of symmetry.

Hold a mirror against each one of the pictures below. Does the mirror show you the missing half of the object? Which objects are symmetrical?

The reflection of this clock is not quite the same as the real clock. Can you see how it is different?

In the mirror, the clock is the right way up but the numbers have changed sides. The reflection is the wrong way round which means you can't read the numbers.

With two mirrors held at an angle in front of the clock, the reflection is the right way round. Can you work out why this happens?

Repeat the investigation yourself. Put your finger to one side of the clock and then the other. Which mirror reflects the left side of the clock; and which the right side?

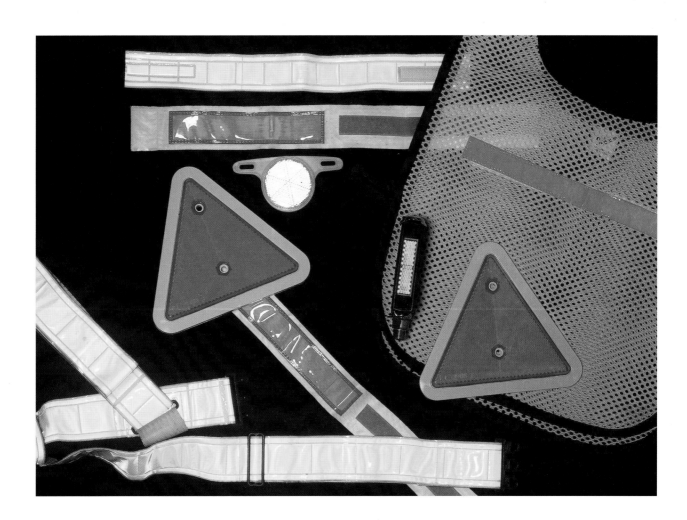

The "reflectors" used on cars and bicycles have many little hollows under the smooth outer surface. They reflect any light that falls on them straight back towards the source of the light. This makes "reflectors" glow almost as brightly as a lamp.

When cycling at night, it is a good idea to wear safety strips which reflect the light from car headlights. Car drivers will be able to see you more easily.

If you hold two mirrors facing each other at an angle, you will see more than one reflection of an object. This is because light bounces to and fro between the mirrors.

If you move the mirrors closer together, you will see more and more reflections. In the picture below, how many bicycles can you see?

Inside a periscope light bounces between two mirrors. This allows a submarine commander to see above the surface of the sea while the submarine is still hidden beneath the waves.

Ask an adult to help you arrange two large mirrors so they are directly facing each other. Stand between the two mirrors. How many reflections can you see stretching away into the distance?

FUZZY LIGHT

Some materials, such as frosted glass or net curtains, reflect some light but also let some light pass through them. These materials are called translucent. Inside translucent materials, the light is scattered in different directions. If you look through translucent materials, everything looks fuzzy.

Why do you think bathroom windows are often made of frosted glass?

Other materials, such as glass or water, let most of the light pass right through them. These materials are called transparent. In the picture of a window on the next page, which material is transparent, which is translucent and which is opaque?

REFLECTIONS ON THE INSIDE

Have you ever looked underneath the surface of water? It looks silvery, like a mirror. This is because the light inside the water is reflected back into the water when it hits the surface layer. Ask a friend to put his or her hand into a transparent tank that is full of water. When you look underneath the surface of the water, how many fingers can you see?

To find out more about the reflections inside water, try this test.

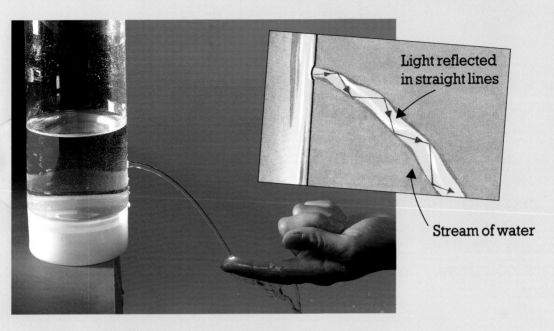

Light reflected in straight lines

Stream of water

1 Make a small hole in one side of a large plastic bottle.

2 Fill the bottle with water and quickly put on the top.

3 Ask a friend to shine a torch through the bottle.

4 Hold the bottle over a bowl or sink and undo the top of the bottle a little so that water comes out of the hole.

5 Put your finger in the water. Can you see light on your finger? Is the light bending?

Optical fibres are thin glass rods that carry light. Inside the fibres light is reflected in straight lines, as in the test above. Optical fibres are used in communication cables and to help surgeons see inside the human body.

BENDING LIGHT

Light travels more slowly through glass or water than it does through air. If light hits glass or water at an angle, this slowing-down makes it change direction. The "bending" of the light is called refraction.

Have you ever looked down at your legs when you are standing in a swimming pool? Refraction makes your legs look shorter than they really are.

Refraction also makes the flower stems in the picture on the next page look as if they are cut in half.

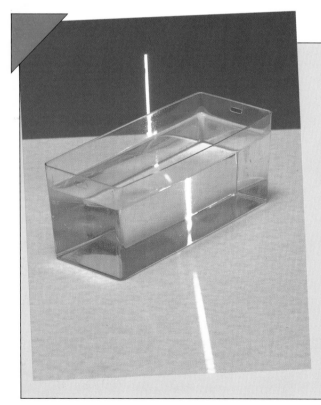

To see refraction in action, try this test.

1 Fill a narrow, transparent glass or plastic tank with water.

2 Cut a slit in a piece of card and stand the card upright a little way away from the tank. Fix the card in position with modelling clay.

3 Shine a torch through the slit. Can you see how the light ray "bends" as it passes through the tank?

BIGGER...

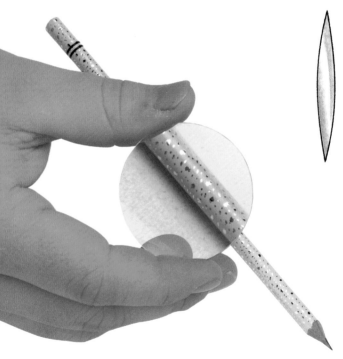

Any piece of transparent material with smoothly curved sides is called a lens. Lenses bend light to make things look bigger or smaller. We have a lens in each eye, but some people need extra lenses to help them see clearly.

People who are long-sighted would not be able to see the car clearly if it was close to them. The car looks out of focus. They wear glasses with a lens that is thicker in the middle than at the edges. This is called a convex lens. It makes things look bigger.

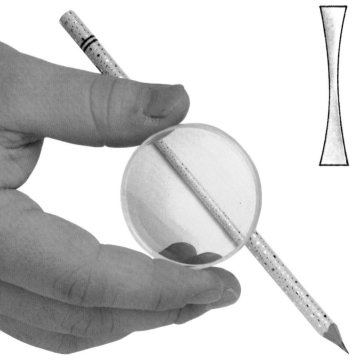

People who are short-sighted would not be able to see the car clearly if it was a long way away. They wear glasses with a lens that is thinner in the middle than at the edges. This is called a concave lens. It makes things look smaller.

A convex or magnifying lens bends light rays inwards so all the light comes together at one point. This is called the focus of the lens. In a camera, the lens brings light to a focus on the film to form a clear image there.

Convex lenses can focus rays of sunlight to produce heat and make things catch fire. Old bottles or broken glass in the countryside can act as convex lenses and start fires. So it is always best to take litter home and put empty bottles in a bottle bank.

How does a concave or hollow lens change the direction of light rays?

This boy is standing behind an unusual lens that can be used as a magnifying glass. It makes the top half of his body look much too big for the bottom half! Instead of having a curved surface, this lens is made from a flat sheet of plastic with tiny steps in it. The steps bend the light as it goes through the lens.

This sort of lens is used in car headlights to make the light spread out in the right direction.

Microscopes use many different lenses to reveal amazing details that we cannot see with our eyes alone. Can you find out the names of some other instruments that have lenses inside them?

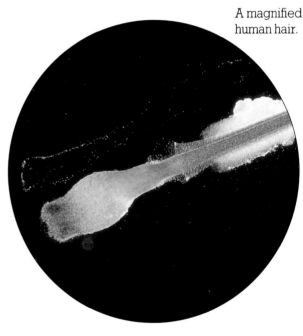

A magnified human hair.

CURVED MIRRORS

Curved mirrors change the size and shape of objects that are reflected in them.

Have you ever looked at your reflection in a spoon? On one side, a spoon is hollow, like a concave mirror. Your reflection looks bigger and it is also upside down!

On the other side, a spoon bulges outwards, like a convex mirror. Convex mirrors make things look smaller. They collect light from a wide area and they give a good view of a large space. They are used in shops, cars and mirror glasses.

Try bending plastic mirror board. What happens to your reflection in this curved mirror?

When convex and concave mirrors are mixed together on one surface, it makes the reflections look very funny!

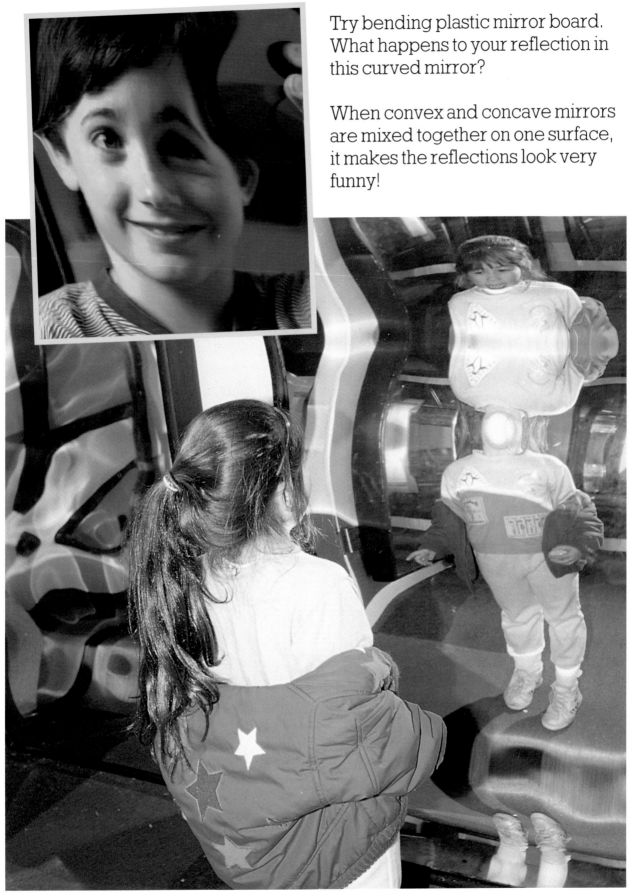

MORE THINGS TO DO

Animal shadows

Ask a friend to hold a torch behind your hands in a darkened room. How many different animal shadows can you make with your hands? Here are some ideas:

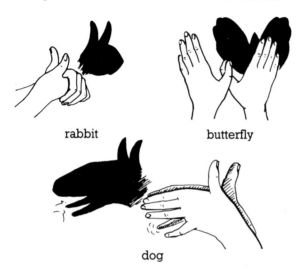

rabbit   butterfly

dog

Draw your shadow

On a sunny day, find a safe area of concrete, such as a playground. (Do not go out in the street to do this.) Ask an adult if you and a friend can use chalk to draw round your shadows.

Stand in the same place in the morning, at midday and in the afternoon. Take it in turns to stand still while one of you chalks round the other's shadow. Are your shadows the same size at different times of day? Think about the position of the Sun in the sky. How does this affect the size of the shadows on the ground?

Looking for mirrors

Look out for mirrors in shops, on cars, on furniture, on buildings, at the dentist or at the fairground. What shapes and sizes are the mirrors? Why are they used?

Make a simple periscope

Use some modelling clay to fix two small mirrors to a 30-centimetre ruler. The mirrors should be facing each other and tilted at a 45° angle. You can use this simple periscope to look over a wall.

Light from objects on the other side of the wall is reflected from the top mirror and then down into the bottom mirror. By looking into the bottom mirror, you can see the hat on the other side of the wall. Can you design a box for your periscope?

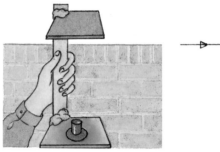
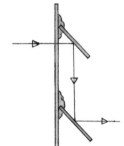

Make a kaleidoscope

You will need three equal-sized mirrors, a piece of white paper, sticky tape and some small, coloured shapes or beads. Ask a friend to hold the three mirrors on the paper so that their sides are touching. Use some sticky tape to fix the mirrors in this position.

Drop the coloured shapes or beads inside the mirrors. How many reflections can you see? When you move the shapes or beads, how does the pattern change?

Collecting materials

Make a collection of transparent, translucent and opaque materials. Look back at pages 6 and 16 for some ideas to get you started. To check whether a material is translucent, shine a light through it. If the light looks blurred, the material is translucent.

Paper is translucent. Shine a light through several sheets of white paper. How many sheets do you need to add before the light disappears?

Mirror maze

Draw two wavy lines a centimetre apart. Prop up a large mirror with books so you can see your maze reflected in it. Now hold up a book so you cannot see the maze but you can see its reflection.

Look at the reflection and use a coloured pencil to try and draw a line through your maze without touching either of the lines. How fast can you do this?

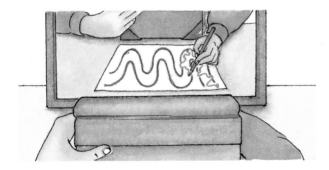

Mirror messages

You can use mirrors to send messages by reflecting the light from the Sun or a torch. Can you invent a code of long or short flashes? A pattern of flashes can stand for a letter or a word. See if you can find out how the Morse code works and use this code to send more detailed messages to your friends.

Bending light trick

Place a coin in a cup and put the cup on the table in front of you. Move the cup away from you until the rim of the cup hides the coin. Keep your head in the same position and slowly pour water into the cup. Soon the coin will appear again, as if by magic.

This happens because the water "bends" (refracts) light from the coin over the rim of the cup and into your eyes.

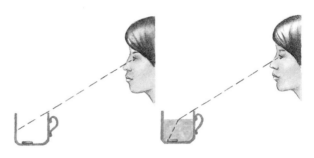

Make a microscope

This simple microscope uses two convex lenses to make things look bigger. It will let you see amazing details that are usually hidden from view.

Put two pencils about four centimetres apart and place an object, such as a feather, between the pencils. Put a piece of clear polythene or plastic (wrap) over the pencils and add a small drop of water on top. This is one convex lens. It makes the object look a bit bigger. Now hold a magnifying glass over the drop of water. This is the second convex lens. How big does the object look this time?

DID YOU KNOW?

▲ The earliest mirrors were made of highly polished metal. The Romans used bronze mirrors.

▲ Many road signs seem to light up at night when car headlights shine on them. This is because there are thousands of glass beads on the signs which reflect the light back into our eyes.

▲ Ambulances have the word AMBULANCE written on the front of the vehicle, but the letters are back to front. When the drivers of other vehicles look in their rear-view mirrors, they will see the word the right way round.

▲ People sometimes see mirages because a layer of very hot air close to the ground "bends" (refracts) light. This is why a dry road sometimes looks wet on a very hot day. The wet, shimmering road is actually a reflection of light from the sky.

▲ The lens in your eye is about the size of a pea. It is made from a clear, rubbery material and can change shape as a result of tiny muscles working in your eye.

▲ Most spiders have eight simple eyes. A fly's eyes are made of tiny eyes each within a lens. They are called compound eyes. Even though they have more eyes than us, spiders and insects cannot see as well as we can.

▲ One optical fibre can carry many thousands of telephone conversations. The sounds of peoples' voices are converted into pulses of light that travel inside the optical fibres. At the end of the fibres, the light pulses are changed back into sounds again.

▲ The glass in optical fibres is so clear that a solid block several kilometres thick would be as easy to see through as an ordinary pane of glass.

▲ The Sun is 150 million kilometres from Earth. It takes sunlight eight minutes to reach us.

▲ In air, light travels at 300,000,000 metres per second. This means it can travel 300 metres (the length of three soccer pitches) in one millionth of a second. In solids and liquids, light travels more slowly. In glass or water, its speed is 200,000,000 metres per second. In diamond, the speed of light is only 120,000,000 metres per second.

▲ A mirror placed on the moon by the Apollo astronauts is used by scientists to measure the distance between Earth and the Moon. Scientists shine a laser beam on to the mirror and time how long it takes to be reflected back to Earth. They know how fast light travels, so they can work out the distance between the Moon and Earth.

▲ Have you ever noticed that you can see your reflection in a window when it's dark outside? The glass reflects light, like a mirror. Two-way mirrors work in a similar way. The mirror has a thin layer of silver on one side, which lets about half the light through and reflects the other half. It is placed between a dark room and a light room. In the light room, a lot of light is reflected back from the surface of the mirror so it is hard to see through into the dark room. But in the dark room, very little light is reflected back from the mirror and the mirror becomes partly "see-through".

GLOSSARY

Concave lens
A lens that is thinner in the middle than at the edges and makes light rays spread out. It usually makes things look smaller.

Convex lens
A lens that is thicker in the middle than at the edges and makes the light rays come closer together. It usually makes things look bigger.

Lens
A piece of transparent material (such as glass) with curved surfaces that makes light rays "bend". A lens makes things look bigger or smaller.

Long-sight
Being unable to see things clearly if they are near to you. Long-sighted people wear glasses with convex lenses.

Magnifying glass
A convex lens that makes things look bigger.

Microscope
An instrument that makes very small objects look much bigger. Many microscopes use lenses to magnify.

Mirror
A smooth, shiny surface that produces good reflections. Mirrors are usually made of flat, smooth glass coated on one side with a layer of shiny metal, such as silver or aluminium.

Opaque
Something that does not allow light to pass through it. We cannot see through opaque objects.

Optical fibres
Very thin rods of glass that are able to carry light over long distances.

Periscope
An instrument that uses mirrors to see objects that are above eye level or out of sight around a corner.

Ray of light
A narrow beam of light travelling in a certain direction.

Reflection
The bouncing-back of rays of light from a surface. Everything reflects some light.

Refraction
The ways rays of light "bend" when they pass from one transparent material to another, for example from air to water. Refraction occurs because light travels faster through some materials than others.

Shadow
A dark area formed behind an object when it blocks out a source of light. Shadows are places where no light falls.

Short-sight
Being unable to see things clearly if they are a long way away. Short-sighted people wear glasses with concave lenses.

Symmetrical object
An object that can be divided by one or more lines into two or more parts which are exactly the same size and shape.

Translucent
Something that lets some light through but scatters the light so that things look blurred. We cannot see clearly through translucent materials.

Transparent
Something that lets light pass through it. We can see clearly through transparent materials.

INDEX